LITTLE
WHITE SQUIRREL'S
SECRET

A Special Place to Practice

BY PENNY L. HUNT
ILLUSTRATED BY THOMAS MCATEER

Copyright © 2005 by Penny L. Hunt   27380-HUNT
Revised March 2008
Library of Congress Number: 2005903048
ISBN: Hardcover   978-0-615-19856-9

This is a work of fiction. Names, characters, places and
incidents either are the product of the author's imagination or
are used fictitiously, and any resemblance to any actual persons,
living or dead, events, or locales is entirely coincidental.

This book was printed in the United States of America by:
The R.L. Bryan Company, Columbia, South Carolina

To order additional copies of this book, contact:
Penny L. Hunt
1-803-275-3377
www.misspennysplace.com

For MILLIE
With all my love,
GRANDMA

LITTLE WHITE SQUIRREL

It was springtime in the mountains.
The sun was shining, the butterflies were flying,
the hummingbirds were humming and everywhere
animals were learning to jump.

Foxes were learning to jump.
Rabbits were learning to jump.
Frogs were learning to jump.

And in the trees the squirrels were learning to jump.
Little Gray Squirrel was jumping.
Little Brown Squirrel was jumping.
Little Black Squirrel and Little Red Squirrel were jumping.

And so was Little White Squirrel.

Sometimes Little Gray Squirrel fell.
Sometimes Little Brown Squirrel fell.
So did Little Black Squirrel and Little Red Squirrel.
Everyone falls sometimes . . .

But, more than sometimes, Little White Squirrel fell.

When the other squirrels fell, hardly anyone noticed.

But, when Little White Squirrel fell, everyone noticed.

And everyone laughed.

Little White Squirrel did not want to jump anymore.
Big, hot hurting tears filled his eyes. He turned and
ran away to hide.

Daddy White Squirrel sat beside him.
"You look so sad. Is something wrong?"
Little White Squirrel hid his face.

Daddy White Squirrel moved closer. "It's the jumping, isn't it?"
Little White Squirrel nodded his head. Daddy White Squirrel was quiet.
Then he said, "I have a secret to share that will help. Tomorrow I will show it to you.
But don't tell anyone. It's a secret!"

At daybreak Daddy White Squirrel led the way.
Together they ran and ran. Deeper and deeper into the forest they went.
"Are we there yet?" Little White Squirrel asked. "Just about,"
said Daddy White Squirrel, and then he stopped.

Little White Squirrel looked around.
"This is it?" he asked. "I don't see anything.
Where is the secret?" "There!" answered Daddy White Squirrel,
pointing down the path. "Just around the corner."

Little White Squirrel hurried past his father, up the path and around the bend. And there it was. The secret. The wonderful, beautiful secret!

He saw something he had never seen before, a tree as white as he was.
"Wow!" cried Little White Squirrel as he scampered up the
trunk and out onto a limb of the blooming dogwood tree.
He sat very still.

"Can you see me?" he called to Daddy White Squirrel.
"I am not sure," answered Daddy White Squirrel.
"Wiggle your tail so I'll know it's you!" Little White Squirrel giggled and
wiggled his tail. Soon he was climbing and jumping all over the tree.

Then it happened! He fell!
He held his breath and waited. But no one laughed.
No one made fun of him. Hardly anyone had noticed!

Day after day he practiced.
Day after day he grew stronger and jumped a little better.

Then one morning Daddy White Squirrel said, "It is time for us to go back and be with the other squirrels". "I don't want to go back!" moaned Little White Squirrel. "No one laughs at me here."

Daddy White Squirrel stood beside him.
"I understand how you feel. But this is a place to practice,
not to live. It is time for us to go."

Little White Squirrel sighed and took one last look at
his special place to practice. Then off they ran,
Daddy White Squirrel and Little White Squirrel,
side-by-side through the forest.

The closer they came to home, the slower Little White Squirrel ran.
Slower and slower he went but soon, like it or not, they were home again.
When the other squirrels saw him, they all stopped and stared.
No one said hello. No one came to be his friend.

Suddenly Little White Squirrel was very tired. His legs felt weak and wobbly. He was just about to rest in the bushes when Daddy White Squirrel sat beside him and whispered something in his ear.

"Remember the secret," he said. "Do not think of anything else.
Remember the secret and keep going. You can do this."

Little White Squirrel took a deep breath and closed his eyes.
He remembered the secret. He remembered what it looked like.
He remembered how it smelled. He remembered how he felt in his special place.
He saw himself jumping and silently thought, "I can do this! I can!"

And he did!

After a while everyone stopped watching. The other squirrels
began to play again and everyone was jumping! Little Gray Squirrel,
Little Brown Squirrel, Little Black Squirrel,
Little Red Squirrel . . .

And Little White Squirrel too.

LITTLE WHITE SQUIRREL

WWW.MISSPENNYSPLACE.COM